Apples for Sheep and Goat

by Rachel Johns
illustrated by Luke Jurevicius

Harcourt
SCHOOL PUBLISHERS

Printed in Mexico

ISBN 10: 0-15-350407-2
ISBN 13: 978-0-15-350407-5

Ordering Options
ISBN 10: 0-15-350332-7 (Grade 2 Below-Level Collection)
ISBN 13: 978-0-15-350332-0 (Grade 2 Below-Level Collection)
ISBN 10: 0-15-357434-8 (package of 5)
ISBN 13: 978-0-15-357434-4 (package of 5)

3 4 5 6 7 8 9 10   050   15 14 13 12 11 10 09 08

"I have had enough grass,"
said Sheep. She saw some apple
trees across the river.

Sheep could not swim, so it was impossible for her to get to the apples.

She found Goat under a tree.

"Goat, look at the lovely apples over there," cried Sheep.

Goat could not believe her eyes.

Goat saw a boat. "We will row
across and get some apples,"
she said.

They got in the boat and began
to row. Soon they got tired.

Farmer saw Goat and Sheep. He
waded out to them and brought the
boat back.
"I do not understand why you are
in a boat," he said.

"Your apples across the river look quite tasty," said Sheep.
Farmer saw the apples. "Now I understand," he said.

Early the next morning, Farmer came in his truck. "We will build a bridge over the river," he said.

Sheep and Goat helped Farmer
build the bridge.

When the bridge was finished, they all walked across it.

After their hard work, the apples
were very tasty.
"I knew they'd taste better than
grass," said Sheep.

Think Critically

1. What did Goat do after Sheep told her about the apples?

2. How did Farmer solve Goat's and Sheep's problem?

3. Why were the apples a very important part of the story?

4. What words would you use to describe Farmer?

5. Do you think Sheep and Goat should have asked Farmer before they tried to cross the river? Why?

 **Social Studies**

Write a Letter Write a letter from Sheep and Goat to Farmer thanking him for his help.

School-Home Connection Tell a family member how Sheep and Goat got the apples. Discuss the ways you like to eat apples.

Word Count: 185